JAZZ
Playalong *for* Saxophone

Fingering Guide

Transposition

The Bb soprano saxophone sounds a major second below the written pitch.
Rule: Written C sounds Bb

Written

Sounds

The Bb tenor saxophone sounds a major ninth below the written pitch.
Rule: Written C sounds Bb

Written

Sounds

The Eb alto saxophone sounds a major sixth below the written pitch.
Rule: Written C sounds Eb

Written

Sounds

The Eb baritone saxophone sounds an octave plus a major sixth below the written pitch.
Rule: Written C sounds Eb

Written

Sounds

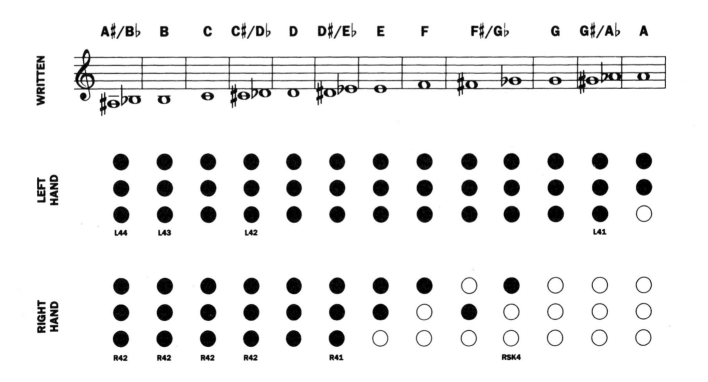

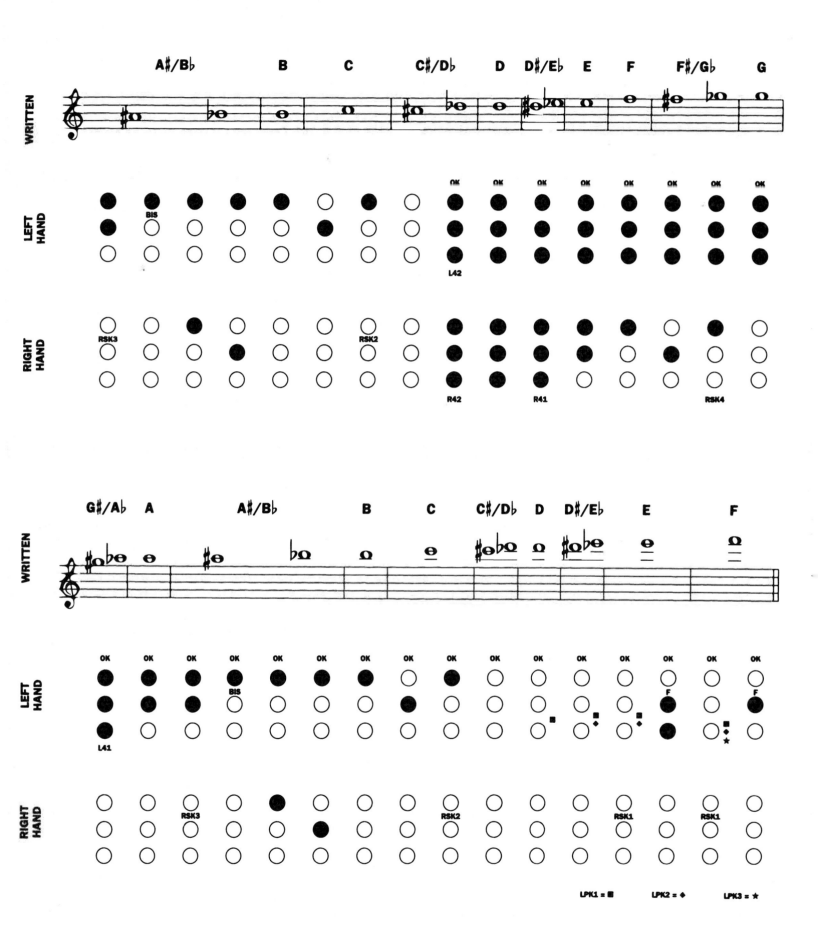

A Night In Tunisia

Music by Frank Paparelli & John 'Dizzy' Gillespie

To Coda ⊕

D. 𝄋 *(with repeat) al Coda*

CODA

f

Bernie's Tune

By Bernie Miller

D.$\%$ (with repeat) al Coda

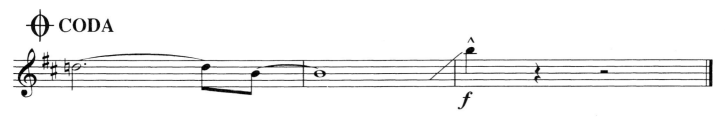

CODA

Fly Me To The Moon
(In Other Words)

Words & Music by Bart Howard

Medium fast (♩ = 88)

D.𝄋 (with repeat) al Coda

⊕ CODA

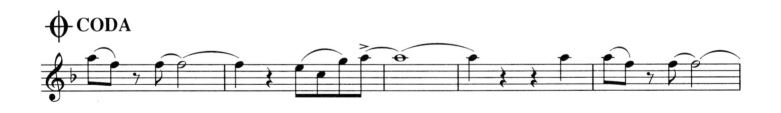

One Note Samba
(Samba De Uma Nota So)

By Antonio Carlos Jobim

Bossa nova ($\quad = 76$)

D. 𝄋 al Coda

CODA

Opus One

Words & Music by Sy Oliver

Medium fast ($\bm{\mathit{d}} = 84$)

To ⊕ *Coda*

Satin Doll

Music by Duke Ellington & Billy Strayhorn

To ⊕ Coda

D. %: al Coda

CODA

mf

Slightly Out Of Tune
(Desafinado)

By Antonio Carlos Jobim

Bossa nova (♩ = 76)

Straight No Chaser

By Thelonious Monk

D.S. *(with repeat) al Coda*

CODA

Take The 'A' Train

Words & Music by Billy Strayhorn

D.% *(with repeats) al Coda*

⊕ CODA

Yardbird Suite

By Charlie Parker

D. 𝄋 (with repeat) al Coda

Full instrumental performances...

1. **A Night In Tunisia**
   (Paparelli/Gillespie) MCA Music Limited.

2. **Bernie's Tune**
   (Miller) Global Music Limited.

3. **Fly Me To The Moon (In Other Words)**
   (Howard) TRO Essex Music Limited.

4. **One Note Samba (Samba De Uma Nota So)**
   (Jobim) MCA Music Limited.

5. **Opus One**
   (Oliver) Peter Maurice Music Company Limited.

6. **Satin Doll**
   (Ellington/Strayhorn) Campbell Connelly & Company Limited.

7. **Slightly Out Of Tune (Desafinado)**
   (Jobim) TRO-Essex Music Limited.

8. **Straight No Chaser**
   (Monk) Bocu Music Limited.

9. **Take The 'A' Train**
   (Strayhorn) Campbell Connelly & Company Limited.

10. **Yardbird Suite**
    (Parker) Global Music Limited.

Backing tracks only...

11. **A Night In Tunisia**
12. **Bernie's Tune**
13. **Fly Me To The Moon (In Other Words)**
14. **One Note Samba (Samba De Uma Nota So)**
15. **Opus One**
16. **Satin Doll**
17. **Slightly Out Of Tune (Desafinado)**
18. **Straight No Chaser**
19. **Take The 'A' Train**
20. **Yardbird Suite**

Exclusive Distributors:
Hal Leonard
7777 West Bluemound Road,
Milwaukee, WI 53213
Email: info@halleonard.com

Hal Leonard Europe Limited
42 Wigmore Street,
Marylebone, London WIU 2RY
Email: info@halleonardeurope.com

Hal Leonard Australia Pty. Ltd.
4 Lentara Court Cheltenham,
Victoria 9132, Australia
Email: info@halleonard.com.au

Order No. AM941721
ISBN 0-7119-6253-7
This book © Copyright 1998 by Hal Leonard

Book design by Michael Bell Design.
Compiled by Peter Evans.
Music arranged by Jack Long & Paul Honey.
Music processed by Enigma Music Production Services.
Cover photography by George Taylor.

CD recorded by Passionhouse Music.
Instrumental solos by John Whelan.
Produced by Paul Honey.

Printed in the EU.

www.halleonard.com